CM00741712

SATVIC FOOD AND HEALTH

In Sathya Sai Baba's own Words

SATVIC FOOD AND HEALTH

for

PARENTS, CHILDREN AND TEACHERS

in Sathya Sai Baba's own Words

Gerard T. Satvic

PUBLISHING

copyright © 1997 G.C. Termorschuizen

Cover design by K.R. Mohan Kumar

First Edition 1995
Revised Edition 1997
Ninth Reprint 2000
Tenth Reprint 2001
Eleventh Reprint 2002
Twelfth Reprint 2004

All rights reserved. This book may not be reproduced in whole or in part, or transmitted in any form, without written permission from the publisher, except by a reviewer who may quote brief passages in a review; nor may any part of this book be reproduced, stored in a retrieval system, or transmitted in any form or by any means electronic, mechanical, photocopying, recording, or other, without written permission from the publisher.

Published by
Sai Towers Publishing

Typeset in **11 point Book Antiqua**

ISBN 81-86822-01-1

Printed and bound in India by Vishruti Prints

The proper care of children is the foundation of a culture

The book and the work it involves
are humbly dedicated to
my most beloved Bhagavan
Sri Sathya Sai Baba
out of gratitude and in love
and service to his creatures

CONTENTS

Preface

Divine Messages of Sri Sathya Sai Baba

APPENDIX: AYURVEDA AND WESTERN NATUROPATHY

1

Preface

"The proper care of children is the foundation of a culture", "prevention is better than cure" and "health is wealth" are golden sayings. Health and happiness go together. Therefore, parents should teach their children, and teachers should instruct their pupils, how to prevent and cure diseases, how to maintain physical and mental health.

It is widely known, both with allopathic doctors and naturopaths that the common state of health, especially of young people, gives rise to great anxiety. Diseases break out at an increasingly younger age. The so-called urban and pollution diseases, such as heart and vascular diseases and cancer, occur more and more. Only due observance of the laws of nature, and God, can prevent these diseases.

Most diseases are toxic diseases caused by an incorrect way of living and eating. Current habits of eating make man ill and weak, shorten his lifespan and form an impediment to his spiritual aims. According to the *Vedas*, in a lifespan of 116 years man has to attain liberation (*moksha*) from slavery to his body.

Modern man has no notion of the importance of ingesting the right food for his health, for the development of his spiritual faculties and for gaining his ultimate goal: becoming conscious of his higher Self (*atma*). Even many spiritual people do not know this. Most people and also many doctors are unacquainted with *ayurveda* and the natural healing arts of the West.

At different places in the world there were and still are naturopaths and institutes. They prove that most diseases are caused by wrong food and, what is more, these diseases can be cured with the right food. In addition, several prominent naturopaths and biochemists say that no single treatment, not even a treatment by a natural healing practitioner, a homoeopath or an acupuncturist, can be effective so long as a good diet is not followed.

Sathya Sai Baba stresses the importance of *satvic* food. With *satvic* food, man can resist most diseases with fair success and attain a longer life. With *satvic* food man has at his disposal more energy and he becomes capable of greater physical and mental efforts.

In *ayurveda* you can find the same teaching as in various important schools of western naturopathy. They all say that food is of paramount importance and that diet is the essence of effective self-care. Therefore, parents, teach your children to eat only *satvic* food, and children, teach your parents to eat only *satvic* food.

According to Sathya Sai Baba living, fresh, raw, uncooked, unirradiated fruits, nuts, coconuts, vegetables, roots, tubers and soaked or just germinating pulses, provided eaten in moderation and grown without the aid of artificial fertilizers and other chemical substances, are the best kind of *satvic* food.

If necessary, the vegetables can be cooked partially, provided they are consumed immediately thereafter. Small quantities of uncooked biological germ-free milk, from cattle tended with love and wisdom, and milk-products prepared from this milk (at a low temp.), such as buttermilk, yogurt, curds and butter, are also *satvic* food; buttermilk is better than milk.

Further, small quantities of starch-containing foodstuffs, such as *ragi* and rice, for example in the form of liquid gruel, or rice soaked in curds. The rice may also be cooked partially. Here, too, it is important that the warm rice be consumed immediately. For hygienic reasons it may sometimes be necessary to cook the food. What is more, a meal can only be called *satvic* if one eats it in limited quantity and in the right mental attitude. Sathya Sai Baba attaches much value to pure water.

This small book consists of sayings and texts of Sathya Sai Baba Himself. You can find these sayings and texts in my book: "*Know Thyself, the Gateway to physical, mental and spiritual Health, Sathya Sai Baba's Messages in His own Words* (400 pages). In "*Know Thyself*" I have always mentioned the exact sources.

I compiled the appendix to help the reader to change over to *satvic* food. By this switch-over the body is rid of poisons.

2

These poisons enter into the blood; this may give rise to all kinds of complications and problems. Besides, most people's digestive system has degenerated by years of eating wrong foods and has become ineffective to digest raw food. So, it is best to change over step by step. Some people manage to switch to *satvic* food overnight. Others take months or even years.

I advise the sick to be guided by an expert (doctor) on naturopathy. Anyhow, everybody should orientate himself as well as he can. It is mostly children who do not have any problem. Therefore, let them start eating *satvic* food early in life.

The best way to regain and maintain physical, mental and spiritual health is to direct one's attention to God and use the four "medicines" of Sri Sathya Sai Baba mentioned on the next page.

3

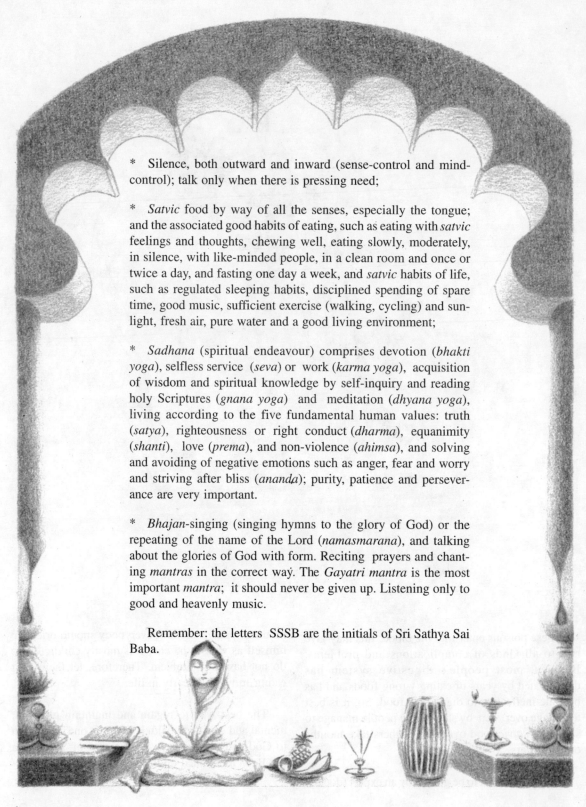

* Silence, both outward and inward (sense-control and mind-control); talk only when there is pressing need;

* *Satvic* food by way of all the senses, especially the tongue; and the associated good habits of eating, such as eating with *satvic* feelings and thoughts, chewing well, eating slowly, moderately, in silence, with like-minded people, in a clean room and once or twice a day, and fasting one day a week, and *satvic* habits of life, such as regulated sleeping habits, disciplined spending of spare time, good music, sufficient exercise (walking, cycling) and sunlight, fresh air, pure water and a good living environment;

* *Sadhana* (spiritual endeavour) comprises devotion (*bhakti yoga*), selfless service (*seva*) or work (*karma yoga*), acquisition of wisdom and spiritual knowledge by self-inquiry and reading holy Scriptures (*gnana yoga*) and meditation (*dhyana yoga*), living according to the five fundamental human values: truth (*satya*), righteousness or right conduct (*dharma*), equanimity (*shanti*), love (*prema*), and non-violence (*ahimsa*), and solving and avoiding of negative emotions such as anger, fear and worry and striving after bliss (*ananda*); purity, patience and perseverance are very important.

* *Bhajan*-singing (singing hymns to the glory of God) or the repeating of the name of the Lord (*namasmarana*), and talking about the glories of God with form. Reciting prayers and chanting *mantras* in the correct way. The *Gayatri mantra* is the most important *mantra*; it should never be given up. Listening only to good and heavenly music.

Remember: the letters SSSB are the initials of Sri Sathya Sai Baba.

I should like to express my acknowledgment and gratitude to all those who have made possible the realization of this book, in particular Martina de Pater who made the beautiful illustrations.

May you all walk in the Light of God and may the Lord bless you all with good health, long life, peace, prosperity and spiritual enlightenment.

Loka samastha sukhino bhavantu
May the inhabitants of all the worlds
have peace and happiness.

Aum namah Shivaya
Aum, bow to God

Gerard T. Satvic
January 1995
HOLLAND

THE DIVINE MESSAGES OF

SRI SATHYA SAI BABA

1. The Moving Temple

All religions teach one basic discipline: the removal from the mind of the blemish of egoism, that of running after little joys. Every religion teaches man to fill his being with the glory of God, and to evict the pettiness of deceit. Every religion trains man in methods of detachment and discrimination, so that he may aim high and attain liberation. Man can liberate himself from the cycle of birth and death through detachment from the senses and attachment to the inquiry into his real nature.

Believe that all hearts are motivated by the one and only God; that all faiths glorify the one and only God; that all names in all languages and all forms can conceive, denote the one and only God; His adoration is best done by means of love. Cultivate the attitude of oneness between men of all creeds, all countries and all continents.

Man does not recognize the disease that is torturing him. The disease is due to "vitamin deficiency", as the Scriptures of all cultures say: the vitamins are *satya* (truth), *dharma* (right conduct, morality), *shanti* (peace), *prema* (love) and *ahimsa* (non-violence). Take them and you recover; assimilate them into your character and conduct and you shine with fine mental and physical health.

Where is God?
God is everywhere! God is omnipresent, omnipotent, omniscient. See God in everything -- in all plants animals. God is in man, no, man himself is God. God is right inside you, if you look with insight.

What is the way to God?
Be good, do good, see good, think good, and talk good. Do no evil, see no evil, hear no evil, think no evil, and talk no evil. Love all, serve all. Service to man is service to God. Righteousness (*dharma*) is harmony of thought, word and deed.

Surrender is to make use of your God-given faculties and energy to perform your legitimate work, dedicating all your activities to the Lord without a false sense of doership and without undue concern for the results of your acts.

Love and serve your parents and your motherland. The body is either strong or weak according to the food, recreations and habits of one's parents. Even though the body is transient you should take good care of it because it is a moving temple of God.

Health is wealth. A sound mind needs a healthy body. Health is the essential prerequisite for success in all aspects of life, for realising the four ideals that should guide humans, namely, moral living (*dharma*), prosperity (*artha*), fulfilling beneficent desires (*kama*) and liberation (*moksha*).

Anger, jealousy, fear, worry, bad thoughts, bad company and bad food are fertile grounds for disease, where it thrives. Many illnesses are produced by wrong food habits. Krishna said: "Moral conduct, good habits, spiritual effort, all depend upon the quality of the food; diseases, mental weakness, spiritual slackness, all are produced by wrong foods".

Food plays a crucial role in determining one's thoughts, feelings, words and actions. Food is the cause of all conflicts. Scriptures classify food as *satvic*, *rajasic* and *tamasic* and relate these types to the three *gunas*. Control your body and senses, conquer your mind, eat in moderation and live long. Eat only *satvic* food; it is conducive to self-realization.

It is wiser to prevent disease than to pursue varied remedies afterwards, when it has grown beyond control. In the past, illness was cured by simple remedies provided by nature, rest, regularizing of diet and also through spiritual discipline.

The name of God is the most reliable and efficient medicine. The best maxims for helping people is: "Help them to help themselves" and "Self-help is the best help".

Education is the most efficient safeguard against physical and mental ill-health. Develop health both in body and mind. I am urging you to do this, for you have still to witness and delight over many more divine plays and miracles of Swami and many more wonders, victories and triumphs among mankind.

2. Body, Mind and Soul

In the beginningless beginning God was one. The thought arose in Him, "I am one, let Me become many". Man is a combination of body, mind (subtle body) and soul (*atma*). It is man's primary duty to look after the body carefully because it enshrines the divine *atma*, the real "I".

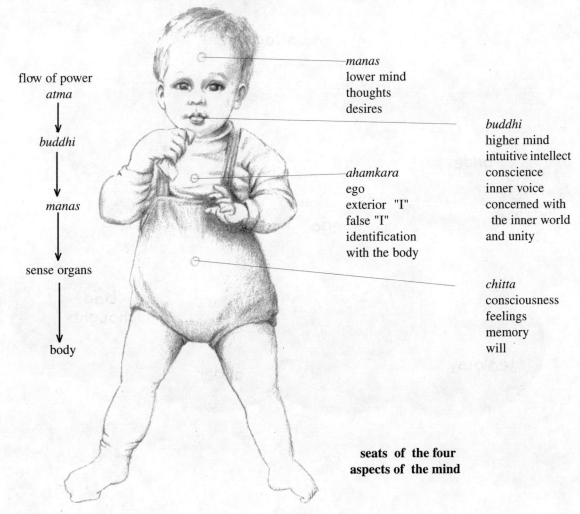

flow of power
atma
↓
buddhi
↓
manas
↓
sense organs
↓
body

manas
lower mind
thoughts
desires

buddhi
higher mind
intuitive intellect
conscience
inner voice
concerned with
 the inner world
and unity

ahamkara
ego
exterior "I"
false "I"
identification
with the body

chitta
consciousness
feelings
memory
will

**seats of the four
aspects of the mind**

7

The physical body and the subtle body (mind), made up of the five elements ether, air, fire, water, and earth, are impermanent. The *atma* is changeless and permanent. Develop the firm convictions "I am neither the body nor the mind, I am the ever-blissful *atma*, I am God". The mind is the abode of all desires, likes, dislikes, attachments and aversions. The mind consists of the lower mind (*manas*), the intuitive intellect (*buddhi*), the ego (*ahamkara*) and the consciousness (*chitta*).

Black clouds darken the sun (atma).
Purify and control your mind!

attachment

desire

pride

ego

bad thoughts

jealousy

anger

However efficient the body (chariot), the sense organs (horses) and the mind (reins) may be, they serve no purpose in the absence of the *buddhi* (charioteer). In life's journey, the *buddhi* is of supreme importance. The *buddhi* has the power of deliberation, discrimination (right-wrong), deep insight, inquiry and impartial judgement.

Since the sense organs are highly potent, the first and foremost task for man is to bring them under his control in order to lead an ideal life. You can derive strength and peace only through love and service along with control of the senses.

9

3. The Three Gunas

The universe is permeated by the Divine in the form of the three qualities (*gunas*): *satva, rajas and tamas*. Men and women are subject to the universal laws of nature. The human mind is activated into dynamic equilibrium by the three *gunas. Tamoguna* gives with the external world; it creates affection and attachment, and so, by means of the dual pulls of happiness and sorrow it plunges man deeper and deeper into activity.

blankness in the mind; *rajoguna* provokes the mind into wandering hither and thither (monkey-mind), and *satvaguna* stills the mind to one-pointed contemplation (concentration).

Only he who is saturated in *satvaguna* can witness the image of the *atma* within. The *rajasic* quality broadens and deepens the contact of the senses

And the *tamas* quality? Well, it blinds the vision, and lowers the *buddhi*, multiplying sloth, sleep and dullness, leading man along the wrong path, away from the goal. The first step in spiritual discipline (*sadhana*) is to put an end to the *tamasic* quality. To remove *rajas* and *tamas* and to promote *satvic* nature, *satvic* food, a favourable environment and good company are essential.

SATVAGUNA	RAJOGUNA	TAMOGUNA
Maheshvara	Vishnu	Brahma
white	red	black
truth, love, righteousness, equanimity, non-violence, wisdom, beauty, goodness, brotherliness, bliss, clarity, tolerance, purity, patience, perseverance, self-confidence, harmony, unity, faith, devotion, holiness	activity, aggression, production of illusions, wilfulness, emotionality, ambition, power, lust, anger, jealousy, pride, malice, hatred, greed, conceit, trickery, likes and dislikes, unrest, haste, adventure, quick temper	passivity, depression, ignorance, fear, attachment, ego, possessiveness, meaninglessness, lack of vision, lowering of the intellect, argumentativeness, stupidity, dullness, sloth, indolence, sleepiness, submission, cruelty, obstinacy
poison in the early stages and nectar while coming to fruition.	in the beginning nectarine, later sliding into misery	unconcerned with the problems of the world, darkness, heedlessness
unselfish, unconditional, divine love (prema)	love for superiors, people in power and rich people	based on physical relations, attachment to one's own kith and kin or possessions, confined to a small circle
4 a.m. - 8 a.m. and 4 p.m. - 8 p.m.	8 a.m. - 4 p.m.	8 p.m. - 4 a.m.

4. Health and Illness

Mental health is preserved and promoted by attention to the three *gunas*: *satva*, *rajas* and *tamas*; physical health by attention to the three humours *vata* (life-force, wind), *pitta* (bile, fire) and *kapha* (phlegm, water). Resort to prayer, to spiritual discipline, to continual repetition of the names of God, and meditation. They are the vitamins you need.

The *Veda*, knowledge, that can confer life (*ayu*) is *ayur-veda*. *Ayurveda* can prolong life, preserve and protect it from hazards. *Ayurveda* deals not only with curing illness, but also with its prevention. *Ayurveda* affirms that purity of mind is essential for good health.

Allopathy does not take into account the roles of the mind and *atma* in the cure of diseases. Allopathy takes the view that only the destruction of disease-causing germs can restore good health. The doctors have to integrate the essence of *ayurveda* and allopathy.

Good and moderate food, moderation in talk, desires and pursuits, contentment with whatever can be earned through honest labour and eagerness to serve others and impart joy to all, these are the most powerful of all tonics and health preservers known to the science of health, *sanatana ayurveda*.

The elders have a great responsibilty towards the generation that is growing up. If the house is filled with the clear fragance of contentment and peace, all its occupants will be happy and healthy. Virtue confers health, freshness, skill and years of youthfulness.

Disease happens for two reasons: faulty food and faulty activities. It is only through food that birds and beasts set their health aright! The body is damaged by food and drink of the *rajasic* and *tamasic* types, and also by *rajasic* and *tamasic* emotions like anger, hatred, greed, etc. (*rajasic*), or sloth, sleep and inactivity (*tamasic*).

Bad thoughts, bad habits, worry, jealousy, despair, all these cause diseases. Fear, anger and affection are the closest comrades of attachment. When you get angry with someone, quietly repeat the name of the Lord, or drink a glass of cold water, or lie down, or go for a long walk, until the fit of fury passes.

Cancer, heart diseases, all these have increased as a result of deleterious habits such as smoking, drinking, sitting long hours in cinemas and theatres, and subjecting oneself to all kinds of shocks and tensions. What is the reason for heart disease? Hurry, worry and curry (fat). Heart disease is more prevalent among non-vegetarians.

5. Control of the Senses

Control of the senses must be the primary aim of men. The senses are the root cause of all the joys and sorrows of mankind. Of all the sense organs, the tongue has an over-riding importance and influence. Mastery of this one organ enables one to master with ease the other sense-organs.

The main door leading to *yoga*, union with God, is control of the tongue. This must be exercised both in the area of taste (food) and in the area of speech. In the Gita, the Lord praises the devotee who has attained complete control of his tongue.

Food is generally looked down upon by

ascetically-minded spiritual aspirants (*sadhakas*) and seekers and treated as something which does not deserve attention. But since the body and the mind are mightily interdependent, no one can afford to neglect it.

Keep your talk strictly under control. Not only exercise silence in the absence of speech, but also be silent in thought. The inner conversation and the controversial chatter continue from morning till night; it causes ill-health and the early setting in of old age.

Today, young people do not know how to sit properly while reading, etc. They sit with their backs bent, which causes various diseases. While walking or sitting, you must be straight as a rod, keeping the spine erect. While sleeping young people should stretch their body straight.

6. A Comprehensive Satvic Diet

A *satvic* diet does not mean simply the food we take through our mouths, but it also means the pure air we breathe in through our nose, the pure vision we see through our eyes, the pure sounds we listen to through our ears and the pure objects we touch through our feet.

Satvic seeing is seeing the beauty of nature, (portraits of) saints and sages, attending festivals in temples.

Satvic smells, *satvic* perfumes, *satvic* food, *satvic* drinks.

Satvic listening is listening to the stories, experiences and messages of saints and sages who aspired to God, who realised Him, *satvic* discourses, *satvic* music, and *satvic* songs.

The sounds, the sights, the impressions, the ideas, the lessons, the contacts, the impacts, all must promote reverence, humility, balance, equanimity and simplicity. The place where one spends one's life also has subtle influences on character and ideals. *Satsang*, or the company of the virtuous, is of supreme importance.

7. Food and Character

Humanity is an inseparable oneness. Still, we see that man has differences of opinion, that there are constant conflicts between different religions, that there are tensions between the castes, and that one country is the enemy of another.

What is the cause of all these conflicts? The cause of all these conflicts and differences of opinion is food (*aharam*). The food that you eat causes all these differences, as it is the food that you eat that determines what you are ultimately.

There are three qualities in the food that you eat: *satva, rajas* and *tamas*. Some people eat only *satvic* food, others just *rajasic* food, while others eat *tamasic* food or combinations. The difference in behaviour is determined by the different food that they eat.

A lasting friendship can only exist if both people eat only *satvic* food. If you wish to have a lasting relationship and friendship with God, your habits and thoughts must be *satvic*. It is the food that determines the condition and form of the mind.

Limited food and *satvic* food are essential for spiritual progress. Spiritual exercises (*sadhana*) will not yield any results unless you change your eating habits. People of all times and from all quarters should strive to eat *satvic* food.

You can recite all the *Vedas*, study the *Vedanta* and exercise every spiritual practice but keep it in mind that all this has to go along with the purifying of one's heart and consciousness and that is where food is of overwhelming importance.

The company in which food is consumed, the place, the vessels in which it is cooked, the emotions that agitate the mind of the person who cooks it and serves it, all these have subtle influences on the nature and emotions of the person who eats the food.

The gross part of the food is excreted as faeces. The subtle part of the food takes the form of blood. The part between the subtle and the gross takes the form of muscles in our bodies. The part that you might call the essence takes the form of the mind.

In the same way, the water that we drink should be pure. If the water is pure, the gross part of it is excreted as urine, and the subtle part forms *prana* (life, life-breath, life-force, essence of life).

Water takes the form of life. Food takes the form of the mind. Now you understand how close the links are between the mind and the food that you eat and drink.

8. The main Cause of Ill-health

What are the main causes of ill-health?
Out of 8,400,000 species of living beings on earth, 8,399,999 species of creatures, like birds and other animals, live on what is provided by God in nature, and hence they do not generally suffer from diseases.

In order to cater to his palate and other senses, man changes the composition and characteristics of the things provided by nature and prepares, through the process of boiling, frying and mixing, concoctions which have no vitality remaining in them.

Birds and beasts do not adopt such destructive

methods. They eat things raw and consume the strength-giving vital essence. So they do not fall victim to the many ills man brings onto himself.

Plant a boiled pulse in the soil: it will not sprout. How, then, can it contribute life to the living? The vitamins and proteins, the valuable ingredients, are destroyed when it is cooked to please the palate. Young people should be satisfied with 2000 calories of food per day. For a healthy life, man needs only 1500 calories of food per day.

Our ancestors used to take food twice a day and

our ancient sages used to eat only once a day. They declared that the man who eats only once a day is a *yogi*, the one who eats twice a day is a *bhogi* (enjoyer) and he who eats thrice a day is a *rogi* (sick).

9. Satvic Food, Rajasic Food, Tamasic Food

What is *satvic* food? Uncooked food, nuts and fruits and uncooked raw pulses just sprouting are the best, and are to be preferred. They ensure a long life. The way of eating pulses like mung, *dal* (lentils), soya bean is to soak them in water and then, when they are chewable, eat them.

The coconut is a good *satvic* food. Coconut kernel, coconut water, uncooked or half-cooked vegetables and greens are good for health. Roots and tubers are *satvic*. Vegetables which grow above ground are more conducive to good mental development than the roots which grow underground.

Flour, milk, fruit and beans are *satvic* food. Buttermilk is better than milk. Food that makes men happy, that is attractive, juicy, oily, nice, tasty and delicious can often be compared to *satvic* food. *Satvic* food can be associated with oil, not with fat!

The older generation in this country (India) used to take a small quantity of rice soaked in curds as their first meal in the morning. It is good *satvic* food; or they drank some *ragi* gruel, which is equally good. Do not eat too much rice.

Drink large quantities of water, boiled and cooked, not during meals, but some time before it or after it. Eat at regular intervals according to a well established time-table. People can live longer and more healthily if only they eat the minimum.

Some people are under the wrong impression that *satvic* food should consist of just milk, yogurt, sweets and fruit. They believe that they will become *satvic* by consuming large amounts of these delicacies. They are absolutely mistaken.

Excessive and immoderate consumption of milk and its products awakens and aggravates the *rajasic* and *tamasic* qualities in man. The quality and quantity of food that we take determine our thoughts and feelings.

The food man partakes of these days is essentially *rajasic* and *tamasic*. This is the reason why there is cruelty and unrest in the mind of men. Their physical health too is poor. The food decides the *guna*, the *guna* seeks the food congenial to it; thus the vicious circle moves on.

You are now feeding the plants, the vegetables with artificial manure and they do not have the innate strength which they ought to have. The present fertilizers are full of defects. As a result, you find an increase in the number of cancer cases and heart complaints.

The main cause of cancer is commercial sugar. Too much medication is also bad. Allow nature full scope to fight the disease and set you right. Adopt more and more the principles of naturopathy, and give up running after doctors. For all diseases the stomach is the key point.

What *is rajasic food?* *Rajasic* food is the opposite of *satvic*. It is too salty, too sweet, too bitter, too hot, too sour, too spicy, too odorous. Such food excites and intoxicates. Also food without oil, which is thus totally dry, must not be eaten. Indians use a lot of *tamarind* which is detrimental to health.

Food that is very hot, spicy or sour can be compared to wine and meat. What you call pickling is literally laying the food in salt. The effect of the salt is worse than that of wine. I advise those with high blood pressure not to use salt because salt pollutes the blood.

Alcoholic drinks and meat-eating promote *rajoguna*. By eating flesh one develops violent tendencies and animal diseases. Meat promotes the demonic qualities in you. It is possible that soldiers in the army need this food, but spiritual aspirants do not.

Besides this, it is significant to note that those who live on vegetarian food are less prone to disease, whereas non-vegetarians are subject to more diseases. Non-vegetarian food not only affects man's body, but also has deleterious effects on the mind.

It is a sin to kill innocent animals for the sake of filling our stomachs. God is in every creature, so how can you give such pain? Animals did not come for the purpose of supplying food to human beings, they came to work out their own life in the world.

What is *tamasic* food? The food that depresses, disrupts, and causes disease is *tamasic*. *Tamasic* food deadens the intuitive intellect (*buddhi*). Excessive food leads to mental derangement. Indulging in a variety of tasty food is *tamasic*.

If you have cooked food, you should not save it for other people; it becomes *tamasic* food. Heated food that has totally cooled down is *tamasic* food. Do not keep food one or two days, or even longer, for it becomes *tamasic* food.

Eat cooked food immediately after it has been cooked. The longer you wait the more *tamasic* the food becomes. Unperishable food such as pop rice is *tamasic*. Food that begins to smell is also *tamasic*. Wine and meat give lots of *tamasic* qualities.

Dirty thoughts come from fish. Fish are *tamasic* items of food. Food with too much fat and starch, which are *tamasic* in their effects on the body, should be avoided. How can you cure diabetes and problems with blood pressure? The golden principle, or formula is diet control!

Those who know that physical health is the greatest treasure take great care to eat only *satvic* food. *Tamasic* and *rajasic* food put the mind in slavery. Eat *satvic* food, then your holy nature will express itself. The holy world comes out of *satvic* food.

10. Purification of Our Food

Just before taking your food, you should pray and offer the entire meal to God, in order to cleanse and purify it; it becomes consecrated food (*prasadam*). Wherever you may go, before eating your food, you should remember the following two verses of the *Gita* and the *Asatoma* prayer.

Brahmarpanam, Brahma havir, Brahmagnau Brahmana hutam; Brahmaiva tena gantavyam, Brahma karma samadhina. IV: 24

The act of offering is *Brahman*, the offering itself is *Brahman*, offered by *Brahman* in the sacred fire which is *Brahman*. He alone attains *Brahman* who, in all his actions, is fully absorbed in *Brahman*.

Aham Vaishvanaro bhutva, praninam dehamashritah, Pranapana sama yuktah, pachami annam chatur vidham. XV: 14

I am *Vaishvanaro*, the all-pervading cosmic energy lodged in the bodies of living beings. Being united with their in-going and out-going life-breaths, I consume all the different (four) types of foods.

Before offering this prayer, the food is merely food, but once you offer it to the Lord it becomes *prasadam* (consecrated food). This prayer removes all the defects and flaws in the vessels and in the articles of food, as well as any negative influence acquired during the cooking process.

The purpose of our chanting the fourteenth verse of the fifteenth chapter of the *Gita* is to obtain success in worldly matters and to overcome the obstacles on the spiritual path. Here, the food we eat determines, in many ways, what we are going to get in future for ourselves. The food we eat determines the type of ideas that sprout in us.

When we take our food, we should not think of other activities and other ideas. While taking our food, if we use exciting words, ideas related to the exciting words will sprout in us. Too much talk while we take our food also causes harm to us.

Asatoma sadgamaya, tamaso ma jyotir gamaya, Mrityor ma amritangamaya, Aum shanti, shanti, shantihi.

Lead me from untruth to truth, from darkness to light, from death to immortality, *Aum* peace, peace, peace.

Before meals you may also chant the *Gayatri mantra*.

11. The Gayatri Mantra

Aum,
Bhur bhuvah svaha,
Tat Savitur Varenyum,
Bhargo Devasya dheemahi,
Dhiyo yo nah prachodayat.

O Mother, Who subsists in all the three *kalas* (time: past, present and future), in all the three *lokas* (worlds: heaven, earth and the lower regions), and in all the three *gunas* (attributes: *satva, rajas* and *tamas*), I pray to Thee to illumine my intellect and dispel my ignorance, as the splendid sunlight dispels all darkness. I pray to Thee to make my intellect serene and bright and enlightened.

Children, right now is the golden time for you. Open your hearts and recite this *mantra* and you will be successful in life. If you chant the *Gayatri mantra* and also respect your parents as God, then the effects of both these will work together, fuse into one and produce a great effect in your lives by giving you splendour and brillance.

The *Gayatri mantra* can be said always and everywhere. I would advise you young people to recite it when you take your bath. Do not sing cheap and defiling songs. The *Gayatri mantra* will protect you from harm wherever you are, in a bus, a railway train, or plane, in a bazaar or on the road. Never give up the *Gayatri mantra*.

The *Gayatri mantra* is an universal prayer, enshrined in the *Vedas*, the most ancient scripture of man. The *Gayatri mantra* has in it the validity of the *Vedas*. It contains the essence of Vedic teachings. The *Gayatri mantra* is considered *Vedashara*; it is the essence of prayer, and prayer fosters and sharpens the knowledge-yielding faculty. The *Gayatri* is described as the mother of all the *Vedas*. One meaning of *Gayatri* is, that it is a *mantra* which protects or fosters the *jivis* (individuals).

18

12. Satvic Food

Food offered to God

that which puts you onto the path of *dharma*

PURE, NATURAL, RAW, UNCOOKED FOOD

raw biological fruit
raw biological nuts (soaked in water)
coconut kernel and fresh coconut milk
raw biological sesame seeds
fresh biological roots and tubers
fresh uncooked biological vegetables
(if necessary half-cooked)
raw biological ground kernels (soaked in water)
raw biological pulses, such as soya beans,
mung beans and lentils (soaked in water)
sprouting pulses
a little rice soaked in water or curds
ragi gruel
foods with natural oil content
a little honey (not heated)
jaggery

a little raw milk (from cattle tended with love
and wisdom)
a little buttermilk
a little yogurt
a little curds
a little butter

buttermilk is better than milk

PURE WATER

PURE AIR

NOT   too much
"   too warm
"   too salty
"   too sweet
"   too sour
"   too bitter
"   too spicy

EAT   moderately
"   in silence
"   at regular intervals
"   slowly
"   in a clean room
"   in good company
"   in the right attitude
    of mind

one meal per day
fast one day during the week
do not drink during meals
drink a lot of pure water
between meals

pure sights, sounds, smells and touches
pure environment

sufficient exercise (walking, cycling)

sufficient rest and sleep

sufficient SUNLIGHT

13. Rajasic Food

Food cultivated with
fertilizers and other
chemicals

heated food

dry food wihout oil
pepper

tamarind

drugs/medication

tobacco
alcoholic drinks

too much milk and milk-products

too much fruit

meat, fish
eggs
coffee, tea
salt

too much
too warm
too salty
too sweet
too sour
too bitter
too spicy

many books, films, magazines
and newspapers

sensuous scenes, exciting sights
aggressive sounds

14. Tamasic Food

Food cultivated with
fertilizers and other
chemicals

heated food that has totally
cooled down (bread, etc.)
most industrial nutrition
artificial food

tamarind

drugs/medication

tobacco
alcoholic drinks

too much milk and milk-products
pasteurized milk and milk-products
too much fruit

meat, fish

coffee, tea,

chocolate
commercial sugar

fat
starch

meaningless questioning
and argumentation

many books, films, magazines
and newspapers

horrifying scenes
offensive smells

Appendix: Ayurveda and Western Naturopathy

These days most people nearly always eat *rajasic* and *tamasic* food: industrialized food, heated and re-heated food, bread, all kinds of stimulants, like alcohol, soft drinks, chocolate, coffee, tea, refined sugar, tobacco, *rajasic* and *tamasic* condiments and salt, besides meat, fish, animal fats and eggs.

Many nuts (mostly heated), vegetables, roots, tubers, cereals, pulses, seeds and milk-products are predominantly *tamasic*. For this there are several causes, such as cultivation with artificial fertilizers and other chemicals such as pesticides, herbicides and fungicides, treatment with many chemicals for storage and transport, irradiation fallout, genetic manipulation, too early harvesting and the selling of stale and old items of food.

In digesting these foods so many toxic substances are released that the body cannot eliminate them. The blood is polluted, putrefaction symptoms appear in the bowels, the tissues acidify and the nervous system degenerates, the body, literally, becomes poisoned and acidified. The immune system of the body thereby becomes undermined, giving all sorts of diseases their chance.

The switch-over from current eating habits, with its food patterns, to *satvic* eating habits and *satvic* food is urgent. Much discipline and perseverance is needed. The goal of this appendix is to teach the necessary knowledge from natural healing arts in order to make the switch-over to *satvic* food as effective as possible.

Sathya Sai Baba has said: "Eat the best food you can find". This is a very important statement. It is difficult to find *satvic* food but, at the same time, it is possible. If possible, cultivate some vegetables and herbs and plant some fruit trees in your garden; have your own goat for milk.

1. Ayurveda

Ayurveda, the science of life, is part of the *Vedas*, the old Scriptures of *Sanatana Dharma*, the eternal religion. *Ayurveda* cannot accept health-care without religion. It states that self-care is the best health-care; spiritual discipline, rest and silence, diet, herbs and simple exercises (*yogasanas*) are its medicines. *Ayurveda* is primarily a *satvic* form of healing, surgery is *rajasic* and drugs are *tamasic* in the long run.

According to *ayurveda* there are three life-forces in the body, or three biological humours. These are called *vata, pitta* and *kapha*. Vata (air, wind) governs our activities and energies, *pitta* (fire, bile) gives us warmth and the capacity to transform substances in the body and *kapha* (water, phlegm) makes up our flesh and secretions. The primary site of *vata* is the colon, of *pitta* the small intestine and of *kapha* the stomach.

Usually one or two humours will predominate. If *vata* predominates we have *a vata* constitution. So there are *vata, pitta, kapha, vata-pitta, vata-kapha,* *pitta-kapha* and *vata-pitta-kapha* constitutions. According to *ayurveda* both mental and physical diseases are from *karmic* causes, accumulation of toxins from indigestion (*ama*), disequilibruim of the three *gunas* and imbalance of the three humours (*doshas*). Most diseases arise from the excesses brought about by the inborn predominant humour(s). The humours are factors of both physical and mental diseases.

Generally, all the diseases an individual is prone to can be treated through methods of balancing the constitution. One method of balancing the three humours is to move from their *tamasic* and *rajasic* sides to their *satvic* side. Here *satvic* food is of paramount importance. A *satvic* diet aids in the tonification and rebuilding of higher quality tissue in the body. *Ayurveda* is concerned primarily with the energetics of food and not with the nutritional requirements, such as vitamins and minerals.

In the first part of this book you have read the teachings of Sathya Sai Baba about *satvic, rajasic*

21

and *tamasic* food. In *ayurveda* there are the same teachings. In *ayurveda* you can find the following additions.

Of the six tastes, only sweet is considered *satvic*. Milk, especially cow's milk, is said to be foremost among the vitalizers and rejuvenators. Buttermilk is considered to be the best in assimilation disorders. Pasteurized milk and other pasteurized dairy products are *tamasic*. Grapes are the best of fruits.

Nuts and seeds are *satvic* in nature. Almonds, walnuts and pine nuts are particularly good. Nuts and seeds go rancid easily, they become *tamasic*; heavily roasted and salted nuts are *tamasic*. Sesame oil, coconut oil and olive oil are good oils. Safflower oil is excessively irritant and provokes all humours. Whole grains are generally *satvic* in nature, especially brown *basmati* rice.

Pungent vegetables - garlic, onions, radishes and chilies - are *rajasic* and *tamasic*. Excess of cabbage family plants - cabbage, broccoli, brussels sprouts and cauliflower to a lesser extent - are *rajasic*. Most beans are *rajasic*. Fried food, mayonnaise, sour cream and vinegar are *rajasic*. Mushrooms are thought to be *tamasic*. White sugar and white flour are *tamasic*.

The spices cardamom, coriander, cumin, fennel, ginger and *turmeric* are *satvic*; most other spices such as *asafoetida*, black pepper, cayenne, cinnamon and mustard are *rajasic*. Tamarind is *rajasic* and *tamasic*. Sathya Sai Baba has emphatically said: "Indians use a lot of *tamarind* which is detrimental to health". Nutmeg and valerian are *tamasic*.

Satvic herbs are: aloe gel, *amalaki, ashwagandha, astragalus*, holy basil (*tulsi*), *bhringaraj, calamus*, camomile, celery, comfrey root, *ginseng, gotu kola* (*brahmi*), *guduchi, guggul, haritaki, jatamansi*, lotus, mint, rose, saffron, *sandalwood, sakhapushpi* and *shatavari*.

Satvic rasayanas (rejuvenators) are: *ashwagandha* compound, *Brahma rasayan, chyavan prash, shatavari* compound, *shilajit* and *triphala*.

Eat in proportion. Eat after digestion of the previous meal. Do not talk or laugh while eating.

Ayurveda

2. Western Naturopathy and Uncooked Food

In natural food diet, and the nutritional therapy of western *naturopathy*, plain, raw, biological food is central. Uncooked food has been eaten all over the world since time immemorial. Food is ranged under uncooked food when during the preparation temperatures over 40°C have been avoided.

The temperature of our body is 37°C. At that temperature foodstuffs are not damaged while being digested. Above 40°C injury sets in. The boiling temperature of water is about 100°C. The frying temperature of butter, oil and fat lies above 200°C. At these temperatures several nutritious substances are partially or totally lost.

The most important food components are proteins, carbohydrates (starch and sugars), oils and fats, enzymes, vitamins, minerals, trace elements, fibres, flavourings and water. When food is cooked about 85% of the extant nutritious substances are destroyed or made useless to the body.

A living body is held together by living food which contains much water. This water is necessary for the transporting of the various foodstuffs to the body cells and for the expulsion of poisonous waste products. Fresh fruit and vegetables contain all the necessary materials for the body and much water. Uncooked food has great healing power.

3. The Natural Physical Cycles

In each day of one's food intake and digestion there are three natural physical cycles distinguishable:

Cycle 1: 12 noon to 8 p.m.: food intake (eating and digestion)
Cycle 2: 8 p.m. to 4 a.m.: assimilation (absorption and use)
Cycle 3: 4 a.m. to 12 noon: elimination (of bodily waste and food remnants)

A well-combined meal will stay in the stomach for about three hours. A faultily combined meal may stay in the stomach as much as twelve hours. Therefore, eat good living food and bear in mind the principle of the proper food combinations. Moreover, eat in the evening as early as possible.

The best times to eat are from 12 noon to 2 p.m. and from 5 p.m. to 7 p.m. It is good to keep five hours between meals. It is very beneficial to cut out the tra-

ditional breakfast and to eat nothing or only fruit before twelve o'clock noon. Whole fruits are better than their juices.

Probably noon is the best time for a starchy meal , whereas, in the evening, it would be best to take a protein meal. Do not drink during meals. You can drink water fifteen minutes before a meal. Drink always pure water. When you follow up the alimentary rules and you have a full night's rest, the body is able to finish the assimilation cycle at 4 a.m.

The shorter the transit time, or stay, in the digestive tract, the better. The normal transit time is twelve hours. Many people have a much too long transit time. Healthy people have three motions a day. Then the faeces is odourless, pulpy, homogeneous and light in colour. The faeces shows us the quality of the digestion. Bear in mind: most diseases arise from poor or wrong functioning of the digestive system!

The switch-over from cooked (dead) to raw (living) food cannot in many cases be done overnight, we need time for that. For a number of people it can be a long time, because their intestines are degenerated in such a way that they work insufficiently. Step by step more heated foods should be replaced by living food. Raw food should be eaten slowly and masticated very well.

Depending on your age and the quantity of toxins stored up in your body, the change-over to uncooked food, especially in the beginning, will entail more or less discomfort. You may get headaches or other pains, you may feel, all of a sudden, tired and frightened, turn giddy, get a thin motion, get irritable or depressive and even fall ill. The discomforts may last a few days or even a few months.

The mix of foods should contain all necessary nutrients. Fruit, vegetables and nuts contain everything that the body needs. We only run the risk of getting a shortage of vitamin B12 when we switch over to an exclusively vegetable diet, because vitamin B12 is especially found in meat, fish, eggs and dairy products. If we use some dairy products we will not need meat, fish or eggs.

Generally, the switch-over to raw fruit is not difficult; fruit is the easiest food to digest. Eat fruit always slowly and chew well. The switch-over to uncooked vegetables is much more difficult for most people. Raw leafy vegetables, like endive, cabbage, lettuce, lamb's lettuce and witloof chicory are difficult to digest and may cause all sorts of problems. All these vegetables should be very well sliced and, preferably, eaten together with mashed or steamed potatoes.

How should fruit be eaten in a proper way? In the first place: fresh! And that also applies to fruit juices. Baked apples, all canned fruit, cooked apple sauce and fruit tarts are all injurious to health. Raw fruit has a great detoxifying effect because of the high percentage of water and the abundance of enzymes,

vitamins and minerals in it. Because of this, it is a very suitable food to eat in the morning hours (elimination time). Forget the traditional breakfast and eat nothing or only fruit before noon.

Fruit stays for twenty to thirty minutes in the stomach; bananas, dates and dried fruit for fifty to sixty minutes. Do not eat fruit with or immediately after eating anything else. If you do, the fruit will be held up in the stomach by the other food; as a result the fruit may start fermenting and producing all kinds of toxins. In consequence of this the other food goes bad as well, especially in the intestines.

Hence the golden rule: "Take fruit and fruit juice only on an empty stomach". Do not eat any fruit between meals and no fruit juice either. Switching over to uncooked food should be done step by step. Applying the correct fruit consumption by dropping the traditional breakfast is probably the best first step.

5. The second Step towards raw Food

VICTORY

Second Step

First Step

If processed and wrongly combined food is digested, then, under the influence of fermentative and putrefactive bacteria in the gastric-intestinal canal, various toxins will develop there. The carbohydrates (starch and sugar) may begin to ferment, while the proteins may start rotting.

Therefore it is advisable to stop little by little the use of processed food, that is, no refined, bleached, preserved, potted, tinned, smoked, chemically treated and bottled foodstuffs. Also the use of alcohol, vinegar, soft drinks, coffee, tea and chocolate should be cut out.

The same applies to the use of refined sugar, kitchen salt and the *rajasic* and *tamasic* spices. Refined sugar is extremely injurious to one's health. Do not drink coffee and tea; there are many types of good herbal teas. *Asafoetida*, black pepper, cayenne, cinnamon, cloves, mustard, nutmeg and *tamarind* should be replaced by *satvic* spices and herbs.

There is no healthier goal than trying to stop smoking. Do not eat meat and fish and eggs. The only effect that meat and fish have on our health is that they diminish it. Among other things, owing to the fat content, meat causes all forms of cancer, hypertension and heart-attacks.

It is not necessary for man to eat meat and fish. We only need a little protein: probably just 25 - 50 grams per day. Cow's milk, nuts, fruits and vegetables contain proteins. Fried eggs are very difficult to digest. Pasteurized, sterilized and UHT-milk, and their by-products, are connected to a large number of diseases; do not use them.

6. Classification of Food

All foodstuffs contain proteins, starch, sugars, fats and free acids in a specific ratio. Mostly, one of these five nutritious substances dominates. Such a nutritious substance is called a dominant. In a foodstuff rich in protein, protein is the dominant. So there is food rich in protein, food rich in starch, etc.

* Food rich in protein. If food contains more than 10% protein it is called food rich in protein. We distinguish between animal proteins present in meat, fish and shell-fish, milk proteins in milk, buttermilk, yogurt, cheese, curds and eggs, and vegetable proteins in groundnuts, nuts, cereals, pulses and seeds.

* Food rich in starch. Starchy foodstuffs are cereals (wheat, rye, oats, barley, maize), rice, buckwheat, bread, biscuits, pastry, spaghetti, macaroni, potatoes, chestnuts, ginger, horse-radish, peas, chick-peas, soya beans and lentils. Mildly starchy foodstuffs are garlic, pumpkin, black radish, radish, kohlrabi (turnip-cabbage), chicory, asparagus, endive, paprika and parsley.

* Food rich in sugar. All kinds of milk contain milk sugar (lactose). Industrial sugar is found in syrups, chocolate, jams, sweets, soft drinks, etc. The following fruits contain more than 10% sugars: dried fruit, bananas, bilberries, rose-hip, grapes, kaki, mirabelles, greengages, figs, mangoes, cherries, nectarines, honey-melons and plums.

* Food rich in fat. We distinguish between animal fats present in meat and fish, milk fats in milk and milk-products, and vegetable fats in margarine, safflower oil, soya bean (oil), palm-kernel (oil), sunflower seed (oil), cotton seed (oil), olive (oil), maize (oil), linseed (oil), sesame seed (oil), nut (oil), groundnut (oil), coconut (oil), avocadoes, etc.

* Food rich in acid. There are acidic expedients like vinegar and leaven, sour soft drinks, wines, beer, etc., lactic acid vegetables and mildly acidic, semi-acidic and acidic fruit. For example, papaya, mango, banana, grape, peach, orange and pineapple are mildly acidic; apricot, kiwi and grapefruit are semi-acidic.

7. The Principle of Correct Food Combinations

The right way of food combination plays a prominent part in having an optimum digestion and the right body-weight. Good food combinations lead to a maximum amount of energy, form minimal amounts of toxins, stimulate the detoxification of the body, and prevent all kinds of digestive upsets and diseases. The proper fruit consumption is the very first and important rule about food combination.

If various articles of food are combined, several dominants can be present; these dominants can counteract each other and cause serious digestive problems resulting in fermentation of the carbohydrates (starch and sugars) and putrefaction of the proteins and thence sleep disturbances, flatulence, acid eructations, distension of the stomach and intestines, food allergy, corpulence, constipation, fermenting diarrhoea, putrefaction diarrhoea and other ailments.

A well-composed meal has one dominant. Our digestive system is not capable of digesting well a meal with several dominants. Pulses have two dominants: starch and proteins. That is the reason why pulses are difficult to digest. Rice is the most easily digestible kind of grain.

There are ten food combinations of paramount importance, four good combinations and six bad combinations. Good combinations are: protein-fat, starch-fat, sugar-free acid, fat-free acid. Bad combinations are: protein-starch, protein-sugar, protein-free acid, starch-sugar, starch-free acid and fat-sugar.

* The digestion of foodstuffs which contain protein as well as fats, like cheese, milk and nuts, needs more time than the digestion of protein food with only very little fat. An abundance of fresh, uncooked leafy vegetables neutralizes this effect. Milk should always be drunk slowly and may not be mixed with other foodstuffs.

* Starchy foods can well be combined with oils and fats like potatoes and cereals, with cream butter or vegetable oils.

* All fruits are by nature sugar-acid combinations.

Acidic, semi-acidic and sweet fruit form good combinations. Yogurt with honey or sweet fruit is a good combination.

* The addition of acid, such as citric acid (lemon juice), makes fat more easily digestible. Acidic oil-sauces form good combinations with vegetables but not with items of food rich in starch or protein.

* Generally speaking, food rich in starch and food rich in protein cannot be combined. Starchy foodstuffs, like potatoes, cereals, spaghetti, macaroni, bread and rice cannot be combined with protein foodstuffs, such as dairy products, soya products, eggs, meat, fish, nuts and pulses. Rice and pulses form an acceptable combination.

* Protein foods and sugar cannot be combined.

* Never combine protein food with acid food, like meat with sour fruit.

* Starchy foodstuffs cannot be combined with beet sugar, cane sugar, jams, syrups, honey, dates, raisins, figs and other fruit. Two different kinds of starchy foods, like potatoes and cereals, can be combined.

* Do not combine potatoes or corn products with vinegar, sour gherkins, fruit, tomatoes, sauerkraut, etc. Spaghetti or macaroni combined with tomatoes and cheese or meat are bad combinations. Leavened bread is a starch-acid combination and because of that difficult to digest. Industrialized sauces are very acid; never use them.

* Fat-sugar combinations are bad food combinations. So do not eat nuts with raisins (matrimony), nut-paste with honey, sweetened cream, ice, marzipan, nougat, etc.

* Raw vegetables are difficult to digest. With an oil-sauce they stay longer in the stomach whereby they can be better digested.

* Waterfruits are considered vegetables. Cucumber, tomato, gherkin, paprika, aubergine, courgette and

pumpkin can be combined with other vegetables. Melon should not be combined with any food, nor with other fruit as well.

* Vegetables and fruits form difficult combinations.

* Vegetables form good combinations with starchy foodstuffs or protein foodstuffs.

* For most people all pulses are difficult to digest and combine badly. Only people with a strong healthy digestive system can digest pulses well, and may combine peanuts, legumes, beans and peas as starch. Eat them in combination with leafy vegetables.

* Combine germinating cereals, pulses and seeds as starchy food or starchy vegetables. Combine sprouts as vegetables.

* The choice of the main course mostly determines the whole meal. A preceding light soup does not influence the main course. Never eat fruit after the main course. Eventually fruit may be eaten as a first course. A good first course is a small dish with raw vegetables. Be careful that in all your meals not more than one nutritious substance dominates.

8. The Fourth Step to Living Food

As has already been said, the best first step is probably practising correct fruit consumption, while the traditional breakfast is cut out. At the same time, or as a second step, all stimulants and processed foodstuffs ought to be cut out. As a third step we have mentioned the application of the principle of correct food combinations.

The fourth and last step is undoubtedly the most difficult step. Bread and other corn products are dead food. In bread, pastry and biscuits animal fats, refined sugar and fruit may have been worked in. Anyhow, do not use white flour and bread, pastry, biscuits, spaghetti, macaroni and *chapatis* made from white flour.

It would be best to bake bread yourself from fresh wholemeal ground by yourself; it is better still to cut it out completely. While bread is still consumed, do not forget to eat uncooked vegetables with the bread. It is better to prepare a thick porridge of freshly ground corn and pure water of no warmer than 40°C.

The grains of corn can also be soaked in water and flocked in a flocker of your own. Do not use industrial flocks. That is dead food. Bread may be buttered. Potatoes should not be fried. It would be best to eat the potatoes uncooked or mushy or very quickly steamed; you may, if necessary, mash them together with butter and hot water. Use only coconut oil, olive oil, ghee or butter for frying.

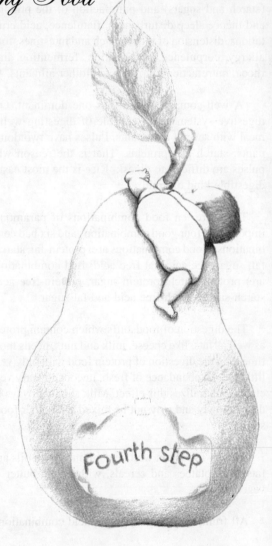

Fourth step

28

We have a group of foods of which the value is increasingly discerned and which are not expensive. It is the germinating cereals, pulses and other seeds. These sprouting natural nutritious sources might be the least polluted foodstuffs we can find at the moment. And it is living food. They are much easier to digest than the non-sprouted ones and contain all the required nutritious substances.

9. Proteins, the Most Important Nutritious Substances

Proteins are indispensable building stones for plants, animals and men. Vegetable proteins are found in nuts, cereals, rice, pulses, groundnuts, seeds, avocadoes and olives and in small quantities also in fruit and vegetables. Half the dry substance of the cells of the body consists of proteins. Very important proteins are the enzymes and certain hormones.

Almonds, peanuts and soya beans are the only vegetable sources of complete protein. The almond is the king of the nuts. A shortage of proteins leads to undernourishment and loss of strength. A surplus of proteins causes all sorts of diseases. Most people in Europe and America eat far too much protein.

Man needs a minimum of 15 grams of protein per day. A good norm is probably 25 - 50 grams per day. Raw food contains highly valuable proteins and leads to a lesser requirement. The better the digestive tract functions, the lower the need for daily protein. Foods rich in protein, such as meat, fish, cheese and pulses, pollute and acidify the body.

Use only raw, fresh, biological milk free of germs and the milk-products prepared from that at a low temperature (lower than 40°C), all produced in very hygienic circumstances. The cattle must be tended with love and wisdom, be fed with good food, and be allowed to die a natural death.

For a baby, mother's milk is the best nourishment. After breast milk they often switch over to cow's milk. In Asia several people fall ill after drinking milk because of lactose intolerance. These people may use milk-products soured by lactic-acid-bacilli, such as yogurt. Lactic-acid-bacilli have a favourable influence on intestinal flora.

Milk cannot be combined with most foodstuffs or with cereals. Buttermilk and yogurt combine well with vegetables, with almost all fruits and with oils and fats. Therefore we prefer soured milk-products like buttermilk, yogurt and curds. Curds may be used for all kinds of sauces.

Curd is a soft cheese; it contains 10% to 15% protein. Low fat curd, or cottage cheese, is a wonderful product. Many sorts of cheese contain as much as 25% protein; that is why the digestion of cheese is particurlarly difficult. Cheese is not fit to be eaten. Never eat fat and old cheese. Never eat bread with cheese.

What nuts have to offer is unbelievable. Nuts are forcing food. It is possible to live exclusively on nuts, fruits and vegetables. Unfortunately, most nuts are peeled, dried and heated. They are dead food. There-fore we should always try to get unhusked nuts. As a source of minerals, nuts (like dried fruits and sea veg-etables) are much better than mineral tablets.

Especially in winter, it is advisable to eat at least thirty grams of raw biologically grown nuts each day. Soak the almonds for about eight hours in pure water. Fresh coconut-milk is very healthy and the pulp of the coconut is rich in selenium which makes it suitable for the building up of the immune system.

Unground sesame seed is indigestable, so it should be ground. Sesame seed is very rich in calcium. Groundnuts (peanuts) are not nuts but pulses; they are nearly always heated. Soak the peanuts in pure water. Further, we have linseed, mustard seed and sunflower kernels.

10. Germinating Cereals, Pulses and Seeds

Many *naturopaths* agree that fruit is the ideal nourishment; they mean fresh, biological, not genetically manipulated fruit that has been grown without chemical fertilizers and insecticides. Unfortunately, this kind of fruit is expensive. Germinating, biologically grown cereals, pulses and seeds and also grasses like wheat-grass are good, fresh

Biological grown lucerne (alfalfa), fenugreek, sesame seed, buckwheat, wheat, aduki beans, mung beans, lentils, soya beans and chickpeas can easily be germinated without the use of soil in a (glass) pot. Germination in a glass pot is the simplest method. First, remove, before germinating, all damaged seeds, because they will rot.

and cheap foodstuffs, containing many vitamins, minerals, enzymes and chlorophyll.

They are also called sprouting vegetables. For very little money one can have a big sprout-salad. Germinating pulses are much more digestible than only soaked or cooked pulses. Germination is a kind of pre-digestion. Germinating cereals, pulses and seeds, baby greens and nuts have regenerating and rejuvenating qualities and are used during the healing of several diseases.

The biogenic method of sprouting of pulses, cereals and seeds consists of five steps:

1. De-chemicalizing. The initial soaking in plenty of tepid water to get rid of the protective inherent chemicals of the pulses, cereals and seeds, as well as the possibly added synthetic chemicals. The water after soaking should be thrown away as it may contain toxic substances. Soya beans need double de-chemicalizing, with additional changes of water.

2. Potentializing. A second soaking in good water, just enough to cover the food and to be absorbed. It

generates plant enzymes end plant hormones, splitting harmful substances and getting rid of them. The remaining water must be eliminated. Soak the smallest seeds for about three hours, the others about twelve hours (hulled buckwheat 15 minutes).

3. Germinating. Cover the pot with a small gauze cloth and put it upside down in the (half-) dark in a tilted tray. Carefully wash the germinating cereals, pulses or seeds gently and regurlarly twice a day. Throw the water away.

4. Sprouting. Further increases of plant enzymes and hormones in the damp darkness creates a complete plant embryo. After three to five days the sprouting cereals, pulses or seeds are ready.

5. Chlorophyllizing (optional). For germinating cereals, pulses and seeds the first four processes are enough, with an additional half day in indirect light, to add some chlorophyll.

Exploring the developed plant embryos to light (not direct sunlight) until they reach a minimum of 5, maximum 10 cm in height, becoming a tender, dark green baby plant (total development in normal temperature, about a week). Baby greens of wheat, rye, barley, buckwheat and sunflower-kernels need a thin, few-cm thick soil to be kept moist for the duration of growth. The baby greens can be harvested twice with a pair of scissors.

Always germinate (sprout) in favourable circumstances: 20 to 25°C, not directly exposed to light, but with sufficient water, sufficient air, etc. Always take cereals, pulses and seeds of the best quality and always of biological quality. Seeds of a bad quality and old seeds rot very soon. Rotting also sets in with too much moisture and unclean water.

11. The Carbohydrates

Starch, cellulose and sugars are carbohydrates. Starchy foodstuffs (especially those made from white flour) , like bread, pastry, biscuits, spaghetti, macaroni and *chapatis*, all refined sugars, including those that are coloured brown, and all alcoholic drinks need large quantities of vitamins and minerals for their digestion and are therefore injurious to health. Avoid them as much as possible.

Satya Sai Baba says that heated food which is thereafter completely chilled is *tamasic*, and that starch has a *tamasic* effect on the body. So, baked bread, and wholemeal bread as well, is *tamasic* food. Bread can be combined with butter and vegetables, but absolutely not with milk, buttermilk, yogurt, curds, cheese, meat, fish, eggs, sesame paste, nut pastes, peanut butter, chocolate, honey, jam, sugar or fruits.

Above all, eat grains in the form of liguid gruel, only soaked or just germinating grains. Always dechemicalize the grains before using. Not all kinds of grains are *satvic*. Probably some kinds of rice, such as *basmati* rice, red rice and *maha sali* rice, *ragi*, millet, blue maize from the Hopi Indians in North America, quinoa from South America, spelt wheat and *kamut* wheat from Egypt are the best grains.

Wholegrain rice (and white rice) may only be eaten very moderately and certainly not every day. The starch from potatoes is easy and quick to digest. Potatoes contain much water, several enzymes and many vitamins and minerals. Potatoes can even be eaten raw. If we eat sufficient fruit, vegetables, potatoes and germinated cereals, pulses and seeds, we have, in fact, no need of grain products like bread, spaghetti, macaroni and *chapatis*.

Energy is essential for a healthy life. We probably need about 200 grams of carbohydrates per day; this produces 800 kcal. 25 to 50 grams of protein per day equal to 100 to 200 kcal; 40 to 80 grams of fats per day equal 400 - 700 kcal. Together this amounts to 1300 - 1700 kcal per day. Sathya Sai Baba says that an adult needs about 1500 kcal per day and young people 2000 kcal per day.

12. Oils end Fats

We distinguish between animal fats, milk fats like butter and cream, mother's milk and vegetable oils and fats. Oils and fats are composed of glycerol and fatty acids. Do not use animal fats. In much processed food, animal fats of a low quality are worked in. We probably need 40 to 80 grams of fat per day.

Sesame oil, olive oil and coconut oil are good oils. Linseed oil has a good effect on the stomach and the intestines. Never fry with vegetable oils that are rich in poly-unsaturated fatty acids such as safflower oil, sunflower oil, soya bean oil and maize sprout oil. Use coconut oil, olive oil, ghee or butter for frying.

Use only vegetable oils of the first cold pressing (maximum 70°C) of biologically grown seeds. The second (hot) pressing goes quite as high as 180°C. In any case do not use extracted and refined oils. Margarine, also from the health shop, is *tamasic* food, dead food. If possible, use oil-containing foodstuffs, like nuts, kernels and seeds, instead of oils.

13. Vitamins, Minerals, Trace Elements, Rough Fibrins

If we eat sufficient fruit, nuts, vegetables and germinated cereals, pulses and seeds, we need, in fact, not worry about a shortage of vitamins, minerals, trace elements and rough fibrins. These foodstuffs contain all the well known vitamins, minerals and trace elements and, undoubtedly, still many more unknown vitamins and substances necessary for life.

By heating food, most enzymes, vitamins, minerals and trace element compounds, rough fibrins and other life-substances are totally or partly destroyed. Some vitamins go to pieces at freezing temperatures, by oxidation, too much sunlight, etc. The outermost leaves of several vegetables contain more vitamins and minerals than the innermost leaves.

There are two groups of vitamins:
* Those vitamins soluble in fat, like vitamins A, D, E, F, and K.
* Those vitamins soluble in water, like vitamins B-complex and C.

Vitamin A is necessary for the growth process of children. Vitamin D is of vital importance to the bones and teeth. The vitamines forming the B-complex family are of paramount importance to life.

Vitamin C is essential to the building-up and maintenance of all organs and tissues; it promotes resistance against infections.

Positive thoughts, feelings and emotions, the vitamins A, B-complex, C, D and E and many minerals and trace elements like magnesium, iron, zinc, selenium and iodine strengthen the immune system.

The immune system controls the growth and repair of all body tissues and protects the body against micro-organism, such as bacteria, moulds and viruses, and also against poisons and cancer cells.

For animals and men, it is very difficult to absorb minerals from mineral water and mineral tablets. Animals and men should eat plants in order to provide for their need of minerals and vitamins. Take care with supplemental (synthetic) vitamins, minerals, etc. An overconsumption of these tablets may cause diseases.

In man a shortage of minerals is mainly caused by:

* A badly functioning digestive tract through which minerals are not absorbed;
* A shortage of vitamins, enzymes and co-enzymes;
* The use of kitchen salt;

* The use of processed food, refined sugar, white flour and alcohol;
* The use of certain medicines.

More and more people have problems with their backs, rheumatism, etc. at an ever younger age. The skeleton of modern man shows symptoms of decline already at the age of twenty-five. This is caused by the consumption of heated food, meat, fish, alcohol, refined sugar, chocolate and wrong and too many grain products. Sesame seed and sweet fruits are the best calcium suppliers besides potatoes, nuts, sea vegetables and milk-products.

Fibrins are found in all fruit, leafy, stalky, root and tuberous plants (vegetables), nuts, cereals, pulses, kernels and seeds. Human food should be rich in fibrins. We need 40 to 60 grams of fibrins per day. Fruit, especially dried fruit, and vegetables are the best sources of fibrins. Dried fruit should always be soaked in pure water for six to twelve hours. In the case of a shortage of fibrins, stool elimination is difficult, the faeces becomes hard.

Fibrins shorten the transit time, or stay, in the digestive tract. Bad food together with few fibrins cause a transit time of two to three days, sometimes even a few weeks. Fibrins absorb toxins and have a great effect upon the feeling of being satisfied. Consequently, the appetite is slowed down. And then it is easy to eat moderately.

14. A few Instructions and Recipes

In most of the following recipes, especially in the sauces, the soups and the vegetable dishes, you can use in moderation (not more than half a teaspoon) *satvic* spices and herbs such as coriander, cumin, ginger and *turmeric* (do not heat them, use them raw). Never use *rajasic* and *tamasic* spices and herbs.

In the morning hours, it is best to have nothing at all or only fruits and fruit juices. Fresh fruit is better than dried fruit. Never use sulphurated dried fruit; and before eating them, let dried fruits like dried apricots, prunes and raisins soak well for about six to twelve hours in pure water. Soaked raisins are good sweeteners. Soaked figs are very tasty as well. Also, when eating fruit, the correct food combinations should be kept in mind. Never eat too much fruit at the same time. Eat fruit slowly and chew well. Do not combine more than three kinds of fruit.

* Fruit whipped cream
For fruit meals at midday and/or in the evening, most kinds of fruit can well be combined with unsweetened whipped cream, about forty grams of whipped cream per person. Fruit rich in sugar forms difficult combinations with whipped cream. Melons cannot be combined. Apart from a little bit of protein and milk sugar, whipped cream contains 36% fat.

* Fruit yogurt
All kinds of fruit, except melons, combine well with yogurt. A deep plate with about 250 grams of yogurt and small pieces of fruit forms a good meal. You can, if necessary, add some whipped cream, and at the same time, some honey and some vegetable oil may be added.

* Fruit curds
Curds and cheese combine well with sour and half-sour fruit, but they form a bad combination with sweet fruits, melons, honey and whipped cream. Curds or soft cheese is easy to digest and contains ten to fourteen per cent protein. It is made by letting the milk go sour and by separating the curds from the liguid (whey). We prefer home-made, skimmed milk curds. It is possible to use cheese instead of curds, but only with skimmed milk young cheese or ripe cheese, not with fat or old cheese by any means.

* Fruit nuts
Nuts can be combined well with sour or half-sour fruits, but not with sweet fruits, melon, honey and whipped cream.

An example for one person: 40 grams of almonds, 10 grams of walnuts, 4 big sweet tangerines. Soak the almonds for about eight hours and the walnuts for about three hours in pure water. Do not forget to refresh the water. Then remove the brown skin from the almonds. Get the pips out of the tangerines and mix two tangerines together with the almonds in a kitchen-blender. Then put the pulp on a plate and mix it with the two other tangerines which, in the meantime, you have cut into pieces. Garnish the plate with walnuts.

A second example for one person: Cut half a melon and a mango into pieces. Cover this with four tablespoons of a freshly ground coconut. Grind with the help of a kitchen-blender.

* Raw soups
Easy to digest, raw soup is a delightful addition to any meal. All kinds of raw soups can be prepared, like cauliflower soup, vegetable soup, tomato soup, carrot soup, etc. They are quick and easy to make. Besides water the following ingredients can be used: fresh potato juice (juicer) in order to thicken the soup, vegetables, some herbs, a little bit of vegetable oil, butter or ghee and, if required, a little bit of kelp powder, tamari or seasalt. Cut up the vegetables and the herbs as finely as possible. Use, if possible, fresh herbs, otherwise dried herbs will do. Suitable to eat are: parsley, celery, dill, thyme, borage, lavender, rosemary, mint, sage, savory, lavas, basil and cumin. Fresh herbs are much better than dried herbs. During the winter you may use warmed but not boiled water. Alternatively, you may pour the soup into a heat-resistant glass container and place it in hot water until it is warmed. Preserve the enzymes and vitamins in the soup by preventing direct contact with the heat source. If you use avocadoes, take only ripe ones. First, warm the water, then dissolve a little bit of kelp powder, tamarin or seasalt in it and add the herbs. If using fresh potato juice, the temperature must be rather high and the juice must be added rapidly (before it turns brown). Stir and finally add the vegetables. The soup should be eaten at body temperature.

An example: Tomato soup
Ingredients for two persons: One to two cups of water, four to eight tomatoes, a small dollop of creamery butter or ghee, one teaspoon of jaggery or unrefined cane sugar, a little bit of kelp powder, tamari or seasalt, and some herbs like basil, sage, thyme, lavas, rosemary, celery, parsley and cumin. Remove the skins from the tomatoes by plunging them into hot water for some seconds (as short as possible). Mix all ingredients, except the creamery butter or ghee, in a kitchen-blender and put the mixture into warm water. Keep the soup warm (body temperature). Garnish the soup with chopped parsley and celery, and a small dollop of creamery butter or ghee.

A second example: Potato soup
Ingredients for two persons: Four cups of warm water, four to eight potatoes, ten to fifty grams of creamery butter, a little bit of kelp powder, tamari or seasalt, some herbs, and, if required, half a teaspoon of cumin ground by yourself. Steam the potatoes in their jackets for five minutes; after that remove the jackets. Mix all ingredients in a kitchen-blender. If using fresh potato juice, the juice must be added rapidly to the mixture of the other ingredients. If required, add some raw vegetables; the vegetables should be cut up as finely as possible. You can use andive, spinach, cauliflower, cucumber, paprika, etc.

* Vegetable dishes
Here we have innumerable possibilities. Of course, we prefer uncooked (biologically grown) vegetables, but half-steamed and half-cooked vegetables can be used as well, especially during the switch-over period from cooked food to uncooked food.

Especially in the beginning it is necessary to be very careful with uncooked vegetables. They are rather difficult to digest and they can cause various intestinal troubles. Therefore it is necessary to chop all raw vegetables very well and preferably eat them together with potato pulp or mashed potato and, later on, possibly, with grated raw potatoes.

They can also be eaten with half-cooked rice and, later on, with raw rice, which should be soaked for 24 - 48 hours or, for instance, millet (soaked for 24 hours). Do not forget to refresh the water for dechemicalization. Use only the best kinds of rice or millet available. Before cooking the rice you should always soak the rice for 24 - 48 hours; five minutes of cooking is then sufficient to get half-cooked rice.

Leafy and stalky vegetables form good combinations with starchy vegetables, potatoes, cereals, bread, rice, olives and avocadoes, nuts and seeds, germinating cereals, pulses and seeds, whipped cream, yogurt, buttermilk, curds, butter, ghee and cold-pressed vegetable oils like olive oil, sesame oil and sunflower oil.

Starchy vegetables are fairly difficult to combine with protein foods, sugar, tomatoes and fruit; they only
combine well with leafy and stalky vegetables, mushrooms, lactic acid vegetables, yogurt, buttermilk, potatoes, cereals, bread, macaroni, spaghetti, *chapati* and oils and fats. Combine leafy and stalky vegetables either with starchy foods or protein foods, for these two kinds of foods are bad to combine with each other.

So, for instance, combine them with potatoes or with yogurt, but not with both. What has been said in the fruit recipes about whipped cream, yogurt, curds, cheese and nuts can also be applied to vegetable meals at noon or in the evening.

The available varieties of potatoes are mostly grown using a variety of chemical aids, like fertilizers, insecticides and pesticides. Hence, always use biological grown potatoes. Per person we can eat 200 to 300 grams potatoes per meal. The uncooked potato is a remedy, especially for heart diseases, stomach complaints, kidney diseases, rheumatic ailments and cancer.

Besides much water the potato contains starch (10% to 20%) which is very easy to digest, 1% to 2% protein, 1% to 2% fibrins and various enzymes. In addition to this, the uncooked potato is rich in vitamins B-complex, A, K, F and C (22 miligrams per 100 grams), further calcium, phosphorus and magnesium (important for the skeleton and the teeth) and aluminium, arsenic, bismuth, gold, cobalt, nickel, iron, silver and zinc.

In a ripened potato is found only a little solanine which, in small quantities, has a curative power; in large quantities it is poisonous. Eat potatoes regularly. In cooking much of the nutritional value is lost,
many vitamins are destroyed and minerals become organically disconnected. In fact, it will be clear that uncooked potatoes are better than cooked potatoes.

At least, we can have a few raw potato pieces with our vegetable meals. The potato pulp is nearest to uncooked potatoes. To make it, first peel and slice the potatoes very thinly, then grind them in a kitchen-blender. Put the ground potatoes immediately into boiling water while stirring and put out the heat as soon as possible. Never cook them.

For preparing mashed potatoes it is best to steam the potatoes in their jackets for five minutes. Before steaming them, cut the potatoes into pieces and, after steaming, remove their jackets. Do not prepare the purée with milk but with boiling hot water and creamery butter.

Steamed potatoes can also be eaten without making them into a purée. Never cook potatoes with household salt, but use herbs like ground dill leaves, or if required a little bit of kelp powder or seasalt. Never eat fried potatoes. Oils and fats which are heated over 180°C are thought to cause cancer. With potatoes and vegetables you can eat some butter or ghee (clarified butter).

* Oil sauces and herbal oil sauces
With vegetables as a binding agent, you can use oil sauces or herbal oil sauces. It is possible to sprinkle the vegetables with a little cold-pressed oil, like olive, sesame or sunflower oil. The term cold-pressed is misleading, for the kernels and seeds are mostly steamed and pressed at a temperature of 60 to 90°C. Hot-pressed oil is pressed at still greater temperature (180°C). In fact, cold-pressed oil is no longer raw food.

An example: simple salad dressing
Ingredients for two persons: two tablespoons of vegetable oil, a teaspoon of savory, a teaspoon of thyme, a teaspoon of sage, a teaspoon of rosemary, two teaspoons of unrefined cane sugar (dried cane juice), a teaspoon of lemon juice and a cup of grated cucumber. Grind all the ingredients and mix them in a kitchen-blender.

A second example: paprika sauce
Ingredients for two persons: one large red paprika, two to four tablespoons of sesame oil, two teaspoons of lavas, two teaspoons of savory, a teaspoon of thyme, a teaspoon of sage, a teaspoon of rosemary, a little bit of ground cumin seed, two teaspoons of unrefined cane sugar, a teaspoon of lemon juice and, if required, some seasalt. Peel the paprika and remove the pips from the paprika. Grind all the ingredients and mix them in a kitchen-blender. In order to thicken the sauce, a large potato cut into pieces can be steamed for five minutes and, after having removed the peels, together with a dollop of butter and hot water, mashed in a blender; then mix this purée with the sauce.

* Cumin potato sauce
Ingredients for two persons: two large potatoes, some butter, two teaspoons of ground cumin seeds, half a teaspoon of savory, half a teaspoon of rosemary, a teaspoon of lavas, a teaspoon of unrefined cane sugar and, if required, a little bit of seasalt. Cut up the potatoes into pieces and steam them for five minutes. Then remove the peels. Now mash the potatoes in a blender together with a dollop of butter and some boiling hot water. Mix the purée with chopped herbs and the ground cumin seed.

* Raw rice porridge
Soak 100 grams basmati rice for 48 hours. Refresh the water after 12, 24 and 36 hours. Grind the rice with some fresh warm tepid water in a blender and add a little honey or unrefined cane sugar. It is also possible to add some butter or ghee. This recipe is only for people with a healthy digestive system!

* Ice cream
Run frozen fruit through high-speed juicer and serve immediately. You can use frozen bananas, mangoes, peaches, strawberries, etc.

Some remarks:
- Avocadoes, bananas, figs, grapes and mangoes contain a lot of enzymes.
- All melons are excellent foods and valuable for their vitamins, minerals, sugars and pure water.
- Dried fruit, such as dried apricots, prunes and raisins, contain a lot of minerals (also iron and zinc). Dried prunes are very rich in iron and silicon.
- Home-made sauerkraut (without salt) is very wholesome. Due to its lactic fermentation and cellulose contents sauerkraut stimulates the growth of friendly, useful intestinal bacteria.
- Flaxseed has the highest vitamin E content of any known seed, excels in complete bulk fibre, is muscilaginous for easy digestion, is high in complete protein and is rich in minerals.
- Jaggery powder and primeval sweetener made from unrefined cane sugar are good sweeteners.
- Kelp is a miracle food having a full complement of naturally chelated minerals. It is rich in iodine. Use kelp powder instead of salt in foods.
- *Chapatis* are better than rolls, common bread, macaroni and spaghetti. They are only heated a short time and can be made just before meal-time and eaten while warm.
- Everyone is unique. The needs of our bodies are different and changeable, so everybody has to find out which foods are the best for him or her, when and where.
- Hygiene is very important. For hygienic reasons it is sometimes necessary to cook the food.

15. Living Food and Motherhood

Should a pregnant woman eat natural, living food? Yes, of course! Pregnancy is a special experience and is a great responsibility. In pregnancy special consciousness of the needs of the mother and the child is required. The mother should have optimum health. This can be guaranteed through good food, sufficient rest, bodily exercise, fresh air and sunlight and a healthy, good attitude to life.

In ample time beforehand, six or more months before the start of pregnancy, a woman's health should be brought to its optimum level. However, it is never too late. Also, during pregnancy, eating habits can be improved carefully step by step. Special attention must be given to the inclination of eating too much.

Eating too much and wrong food combinations cause a shortage of calcium too. Useful calcium is found in sufficient quantities in (germinating) sesame seeds, sweet fruits, nuts, potatoes, cabbage, sea vegetables and figs.

That the natural and ideal food of a baby is its own mother's milk is so obvious it hardly needs stressing.

Human milk is peculiarly and specifically adapted to the needs of the human infant. Mother's milk is readily affected by tobacco, alcohol, coffee, tea, chocolate, narcotics and nearly all drugs; they should be avoided.

The advice is to give exclusively mother's milk during the first year. After that supplemental food, such as fresh fruit juices or cow's milk or goat's milk may be started. Give your baby mother's milk as long as possible. It can be said that the natural nursing period of the human infant ranges from three to five years.

The best substitute of mother's milk and the best supplementary food is fresh fruit juice. Grape juice and orange juice are specially recommended. Give milk and juice at different times. Fruit juice can be given very well between breast-feedings. Other substitutes for mother's milk are cow's milk and goat's milk; they can also be used as supplementary food, if required, alternated with fresh fruit juices.

Never give artificial baby foods; they are dead foods. No other food except milk and fruit juices should be given to the child for the first eighteen months of its life. At about eighteen months of age soft fruits may, however, be added to the diet. Beginning with the second year, fruits, nuts and vegetables may be added to the child's diet. Vegetables may be given raw or half-cooked, preferably raw.

No starchy foods or cereals should be given under two years. It is a mistake to feed starchy food too soon, before the end of the second year. Children under two or three years of age have trouble in converting starch into sugar. They should get their sugar from fruits! Many of the troubles from which children suffer are due to the practice of feeding them starchy food.

Meat should never be fed to a child under six years of age and, better, never at all. For the physical and mental health of the children, it is very important to give them the correct food.

16. Bodily Exercise, Fresh Air, Bathing and Sunlight

For a good functioning of all the bodily-cycles, the heart and blood circulation, it is all-important to combine good eating habits with necessary bodily exercise. Of all possible bodily exercises, walking, especially walking fast, bicycling and swimming are excellent activities. The minimum necessary is a quick walk of twenty minutes. A walk in the woods, along the seaside or a cycling-tour performs wonders for our health.

It is of paramount importance to sleep with an open window at night. The body removes during this time a lot of water and toxins through breathing and the skin; when the body gets fresh air it can function with better effect. Taking a bath or a shower once or twice a day is very good. The rays of light, the heat-rays and other rays of the sun are indispensable to plants, animals and men.

Correct breathing is of paramount importance for physical and mental health. The respiration does not only see to the supply of oxygen and the discharge of carbondioxide and waste products, but also to the supply of *prana* (universal energy). Sources of *prana* are the sunrays, water, air and food. *Prana* is taken up via the skin (sunbath), the tongue (therefore prolonged chewing), the nostrils and the lungs. Correct breathing and having a straight spine in all postures are extremely important.

Sathya Sai Baba says: "It is necessary to cleanse the mirror of the mind of the impurities covering it. This cleansing is done by regulating one's food and other living habits including recreation. This cannot be done in a day or a month. This requires persistent and prolonged practice".

17. Ayurveda and Western Naturopathy

In opposition to western naturopathy, *ayurveda* does not accept health-care without spirituality. *Ayurveda* and western naturopathy agree that the best health-care is self-care. *Ayurveda* emphasizes that correct diet is the essence of self-care, and that wrong diet is the main physical causative factor of disease.

Ayurveda states that things we do for ourselves, such as giving up wrong foods and overcoming negative emotions like anger, fear and worry, will do more for our health in the long run than taking many medicines and consulting various doctors. Spiritual discipline, rest and silence, diet, herbs and simple exercises (*yogasanas*) are the most important medicines of *ayurveda*.

Western *naturopathy* says that most diseases are caused by the accumulations of toxins (toxemia) and the deficiency of nutritional requirements such as enzymes, vitamins and minerals. *Ayurveda* is not as concerned with enzymes, vitamins and minerals, but is primarily concerned with energetics of food. According to *ayurveda,* foods can be classified according to different degrees of increase or reduction of the three biological humours and the three *gunas* in man.

According to *ayurveda*, though mental and physical diseases are of many kinds and pathogens are of many varieties, all are products of disharmonies of the three biological humours (life-energies), *vata*, *pitta* and *kapha*. *Ayurveda* does not treat symptoms, but the underlying causes are dealt with. In balancing the humours the root of the disease process is cut off.

Generally, all the mental and physical diseases an individual is prone to can be treated through methods of balancing the three humours. One method of balancing the three humours is to move from their *tamasic* and *rajasic* sides to their *satvic* side. This should be done with a *satvic* diet, originally devised for the purification of the mind and the practice of *yoga*.

A *satvic* diet is very important in the treatment of mental disorders but also in the treatment of most modern so-called physical diseases. These physical diseases are mostly very strongly related to psychological factors. A *satvic* diet aids in the tonification and rebuilding of higher quality tissue in the body. Eating *satvic* food is tantamount to purification of the mind and healing of the body by balancing the humours, removing the toxins (*ama*), supplying all nutritional requirements and strengthening the immune system.

Most diseases arise from poor or wrong functioning of the digestive system. A *satvic* diet is important, but also the right functioning of the digestive fire (*agni*). *Ayurveda* emphasizes the importance of *agni*. *Agni* not only absorbs nutrients, but also destroys any pathogens. Undigested food becomes like a pathogen in the body, breeding toxins (*ama*) and upsetting the immune system.

The digestive fire should also be fed and cared for to give it the power to adequately digest the food. *Ayurveda* says that spices and herbs are usually the best thing for increasing *agni*. Spices and herbs are also best for destroying accumulations of toxins (*ama*). *Ama* blocks the functioning of *agni* and the assimilation of nutrients. In western *naturopathy* little attention is being paid to the use of spices and herbs.

Ayurveda and western *naturopathy* agree that the modern lifestyle is deleterious to health. Modern life is excessively *rajasic*. We are always entertaining ourselves with reading, television, all kinds of sports and travelling. We do not have time for heart-to-heart communication and for silence, peace and prayer. When we grow old we become more and more *tamasic*. The number of demented people is increasing and is becoming a great problem in modern society.

The food we eat is predominantly *rajasic* and *tamasic*. The mass media as a whole has an influence that strongly aggravates *vata*. Watching television, reading newspapers and magazines, talking and doing business during meals are very bad habits. Meals should not be taken when excessively nervous, thoughtful or worried. Mind-altering drugs, stimulant drugs and pain-relieving drugs are strongly disruptive.

Spices and herbs are like subtle foods. *Ayurveda* teaches that almost everyone should take spices and herbs on a regular basis; they are part of our necessary foodstuffs. Herbal therapy requires the support of the proper food to be effective. Diet can enhance, neutralize or counter the effect of spices and herbs. It may take a month or more of a natural remedy, particularly in treating a long-standing complaint, to have a noticeable effect.

Many old or commercially-prepared herbs may lack the right potency. In some respects it is misleading to speak of the general properties of a herb. These vary according to the way in which the herb is grown, prepared and combined. Miraculous powers can be found in very ordinary herbs when they are specially grown and prepared. Fresh herbs have a special power.

According to *ayurveda* the digestive fire (*agni*) is central to health. When the digestive fire is normal, there is good digestion, circulation and complexion, adequate energy and a strong immune system. When the digestive fire is abnormal, there is poor digestion, poor circulation and bad complexion, offensive body odour, flatulence, constipation, low energy and poor resistance to disease.

Ayurveda says that spices are usually the best thing for increasing the digestive fire, for destroying accumulations of toxins from indigestion (*ama*) and for inhibiting the formation of *ama*. Hence, the right intake of spices can be a major aid in the treatment of most diseases.

When the digestive fire is high, spices should generally be avoided. When the digestive fire is low, all kinds of spices can be taken, but preferably *satvic* spices. When the digestive fire is variable, some spices such as cumin and ginger can be taken. When the digestive fire is normal, mild *satvic* spices - cardamom, coriander, fennel, *turmeric* - can be taken to maintain balance. Use spices always in moderation and knowledgeably.

Sometimes it may be necessary to use *rajasic* and *tamasic* spices, herbs or foods and even allopathic medicines to cure the body, but we must realize that at the same time the mind becomes more *rajasic* and *tamasic*. After the required changes have been brought about we should purify the mind by eating *satvic* food and through other spiritual methods.

Satvic spices can help balance the effect of too much fruit and dairy products. According to the sages of ancient India, milk is an ideal food for children when taken properly and balanced with the right spices. In addition, raw milk free of germs, especially cow's milk, is considered to be the best rejuvenator and vitalizer. Unfortunately, most milk is pasteurized and therefore *tamasic*. Dairy products are *ama*-increasing and mucus-forming, particularly when pasteurized. When you have no other choice, you can add mucus-decreasing spices such as cardamom and ginger to make the milk more digestible.

Warm milk is a good mild sedative promoting sleep. Yogurt is best taken mixed with fresh cucumber and spices such as cumin and coriander. Cheese is the most mucus-forming of all dairy products; here, cumin can be helpful. Children may use *satvic* spices and herbs; the dosage is less with the child's age.

Spices and herbs should be cultivated without fertilizers and other chemicals and should not be irradiated, otherwise they will not be *satvic*. They are used in dishes and in *ayurvedic* medicines. The other ingredients for *ayurvedic* medicines such as ghee, raw sugar or honey should also be *satvic*.

19. Satvic Food and Family Life

Sathya Sai Baba often says: "One who eats three meals a day is a sick person (*rogi*), one who eats twice a day is an enjoyer (*bhogi*); one who eats just once a day is a *yogi*". If you want to be a *yogi*, it is clear what to do. However, most of us are still *bhogis* or more or less *rogis*. Therefore, we are used to eat twice or three times a day.

Satvic food is of paramount importance for our spiritual life and health. Eating *satvic* food is tantamount to purification of the mind and healing of the body by balancing the humours, removing the toxins (*ama*), supplying all required nutritious substances and strengthening the immune system. For a devotee of God it becomes necessary to switch over to *satvic* food.

When we are ill we shall have to detoxify our body and mind thoroughly and switch over to *satvic* food step by step, using the kitchen-blender. Blending is more efficient than simple chewing and mixing in the stomach. Blended foods can restore health much quicker than eating the foods as salads. Eating nutritionally balanced food in a blended form is a big help to the digestive system and also to the immune system.

When we are relatively healthy, we may have to do the same thing but the purification is easier; in any case, it will be necessary to use enemas to cleanse our colon and occasionally the blender to help our digestive system.

Many people believe that it is not possible to live on *satvic* food in a family. That is totally untrue. Everyone can cut out the usual breakfast and, instead, eat some fruit or some gruel made of pure water, fresh ground grain, such as wheat or *ragi,* and some raw honey or jaggery. Do not forget to de-chemicalize the grains.

Everyone can prepare meals according to the recipes in chapter fourteen. To most of these recipes, especially to the sauces, soups and vegetable dishes, you can add *satvic* spices and herbs - as a matter of course in moderation (not more than half a teaspoon) - such as cardamom, coriander, cumin, fennel, ginger and *turmeric*. With these spices you feed the digestive fire (*agni*).

In *ayurveda* it is said that *turmeric* destroys the process of aging and fills the body with youthful vitality. Whether it be North Indian or South Indian, all Indian cuisine has *turmeric* as an indispensable item. Besides making the vegetables and other foods aromatic and aesthetically more tempting, it is the antiseptic effect of *turmeric* that preserves the food from a variety of small insects that can pollute food.

Do not use *rajasic* spices such as *asafoetida*, black pepper, cayenne, cinnamon, cloves and mustard and *tamasic* spices such as nutmeg and valerian. *Tamarind* is *rajasic* and *tamasic*. The pungent vegetables chilies, garlic, onions and radishes are *rajasic* and *tamasic*; avoid them as much as possible.

For family life you can prepare all kinds of tasty vegetable dishes consisting of half-steamed/half-cooked potatoes, potato pulp or half-cooked rice and half-steamed/half-cooked or raw vegetables with oil sauces, herbal oil sauces or curries. You can make a good curry from tomatoes, ghee, *turmeric* and coriander.

Use just germinating cereals, pulses and seeds and baby greens such as sunflower and buckwheat baby greens (chapter 10). There are many possibilities; use your own creativity.

The following guidelines are important:

1. Never forget to pray and to offer the food to God before eating it.
2. Eat in silence, with *satvic* feelings and thoughts, in good company, in a clean room, slowly and at regular intervals and chew the food well.
3. Always eat in moderation, never over-eat.
4. Eat the best food you can find and afford.
5. Heat your food as little as possible, never reheat it. Eat preferably uncooked food.
6. Use the kitchen-blender if necessary; avoid pure juices but blend instead.
7. Do not forget the rules for correct food combinations.
8. Use moderate amounts of *satvic* spices and herbs to feed the digestive fire.
9. The mix of foods should contain all necessary nutrients.
10. Fast one day a week.
11. Drink pure water, herbal teas, blended fruit or almond milk (blend soaked almonds with pure water).
12. Eat cereals in the form of liquid gruel, only soaked or just germinating.
13. Fruit and several milk-products are *satvic* provided eaten in moderation and cultivated/made in the correct way.
14. The switch-over to *satvic* food should be done step by step, carefully and with the necessary knowledge and guidance. Do not forget that everyone is unique and that the needs of our bodies are different and changeable.

Avoid as much as possible the following foodstuffs:

1. Food cultivated with fertilizers and other chemicals.
2. Food treated with chemicals for storage and transport purposes.
3. Processed industrialized food.
4. Old, stale and reheated food. Never put heated food into the refrigerator and reheat it after some time for a meal.
5. Heated food that has totally cooled down (bread, etc.).
6. Fried, grilled and roasted food.
7. Alcoholic drinks and soft drinks such as cola.
8. Tobacco and drugs (dope).
9. Animal fats, margarine, meat, fish, shell-fish and eggs.
10. Refined sugar, sweets and commercial ice.
11. Chocolate, coffee (also substitutes) and tea.
12. White flour and products made of white flour such as bread, biscuits, pastries, pancakes, macaroni, spaghetti and *chapatis*. If possible, also avoid whole-meal bread.
13. Pasteurized, sterilized and UHT-milk and their by-products.
14. Salt, vinegar, industrialized sauces and *rajasic* and *tamasic* spices and herbs.